MW00782575

The Joy of
100
Best Loved
Piano Classics

Selected and edited by Denes Agay

Order No. YK 21909
US International Standard Book Number: 0.8256.8107.3
UK International Standard Book Number: 0.7119.7631.7

Exclusive Distributors:
Music Sales Corporation
257 Park Avenue South, New York, NY 10010 USA
Music Sales Limited
8/9 Frith Street, London W1V 5TZ England
Music Sales Pty. Limited
120 Rothschild Street, Rosebery, Sydney, NSW 2018, Australia

Printed in the United States of America by
Vicks Lithograph and Printing Corporation

Yorktown Music Press, Inc.
New York/London/Paris/Sydney/Copenhagen/Madrid

Contents

Trumpet Tune

Henry Purcell
(1659–1695)

Minuet
from the Notebook for Anna Magdalena Bach

Johann Sebastian Bach
(1685–1750)

Menuett

George Frideric Handel
(1685–1759)

Noël

Louis-Claude Daquin
(1694–1772)

8

Entrée
from the Notebook for Wolfgang

Leopold Mozart
(1719–1787)

Musette

Johann Sebastian Bach
(1685–1750)

Andante pastorale

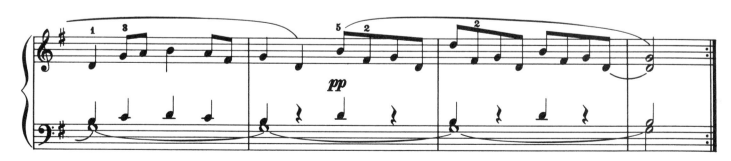

Gavotte D.C. al Fine

Rondino

Jean Philippe Rameau
(1683–1764)

Moderato

March
from the Notebook for Anna Magdalena Bach

Johann Sebastian Bach
(1685–1750)

Musette
from the Notebook for Anna Magdalena Bach

Johann Sebastian Bach
(1685–1750)

Little Prelude In C

Johann Sebastian Bach
(1685–1750)

Allegro moderato

Arioso
"Largo" from Clavier Concerto in F minor

Johann Sebastian Bach
(1685–1750)

Original key is A♭. In the left hand we incorporated the pizzicato chords of the strings.

Gavotte and Variation

George Frideric Handel
(1685–1759)

Variation

Praeludium
from The Well-Tempered Clavier

Johann Sebastian Bach
(1685–1750)

Allegro moderato

Air

from Water Music

George Frideric Handel
(1685–1759)

Hornpipe
from Water Music

George Frideric Handel
(1685–1759)

Rondo Espressivo
from Sonata in B minor

Carl Philipp Emanuel Bach
(1714–1788)

Andantino cantabile

Hornpipe

Henry Purcell
(1659–1695)

Intrada

Christoph Graupner
(1683–1760)

Fughetta

Johann Sebastian Bach
(1685–1750)

Tambourin

Jean Philippe Rameau
(1683–1764)

*Play all ornaments on the beat

The Harmonious Blacksmith

"Air and Variation" from Suite No. 5

George Frideric Handel
(1685–1759)

Burlesca

Georg Philipp Telemann
(1681–1763)

Solfeggio

Carl Philipp Emanuel Bach
(1714–1788)

Minuet

Wolfgang Amadeus Mozart, K. 6
(1756–1791)

Andante grazioso

Quadrille

Joseph Haydn
(1732–1809)

Allegretto

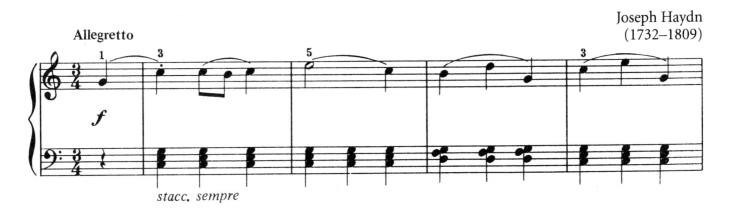

stacc. sempre

Country Waltz

Joseph Haydn
(1732–1809)

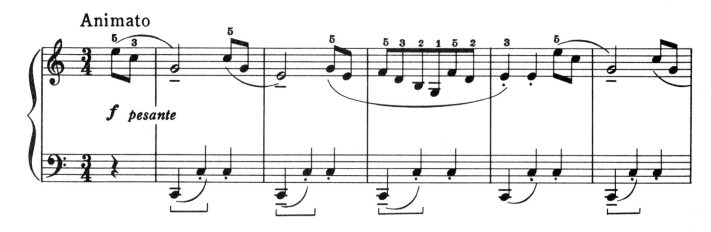

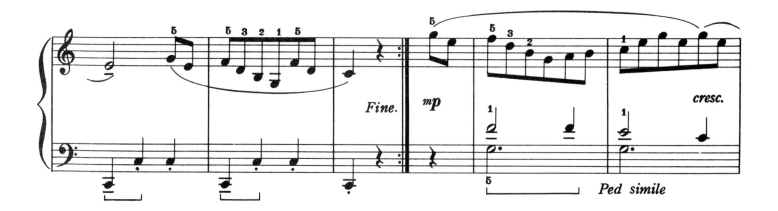

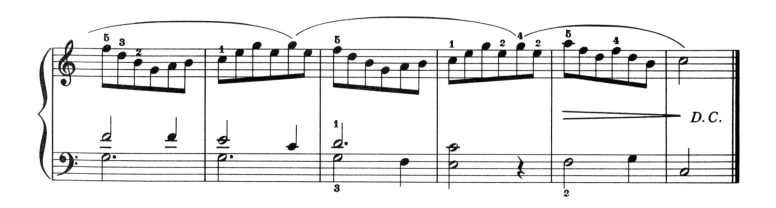

Ecossaise In G

Ludwig van Beethoven
(1770–1827)

German Dance

Joseph Haydn
(1732–1809)

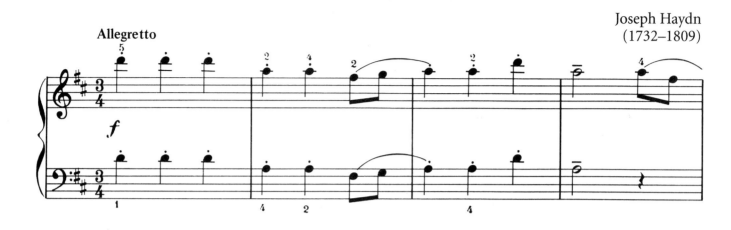

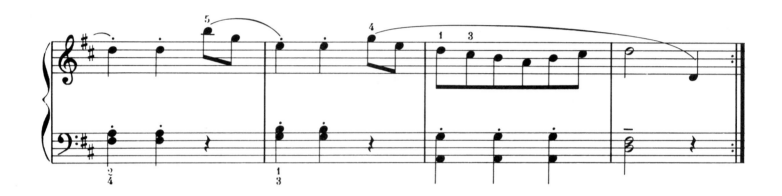

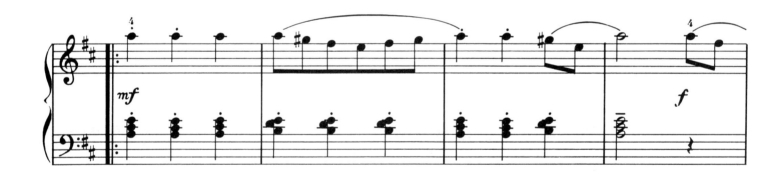

Ländler

Franz Schubert
(1797–1828)

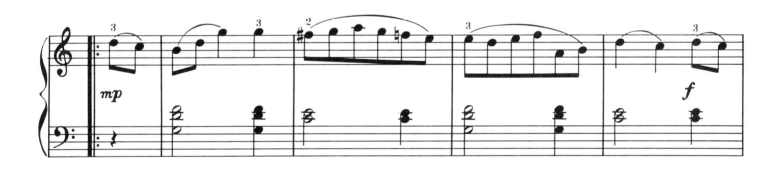

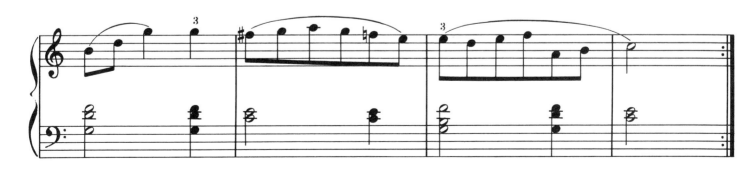

Zingarese

Gypsy Dance

Joseph Haydn
(1732–1809)

Trio

D.C. al Fine

Sonatina
first movement

Muzio Clementi, Op. 36, No. 1
(1752–1832)

Allegro moderato

Alexander March

**Piano version by
Carl Czerny**

Ludwig van Beethoven
(1770–1827)

Russian Folk Song

Ludwig van Beethoven
(1770–1827)

Sonatina

Ludwig van Beethoven
(1770–1827)

Romanze
Allegretto

Spring Song

Come, Sweet May

Wolfgang Amadeus Mozart, K. 596
(1751–1791)

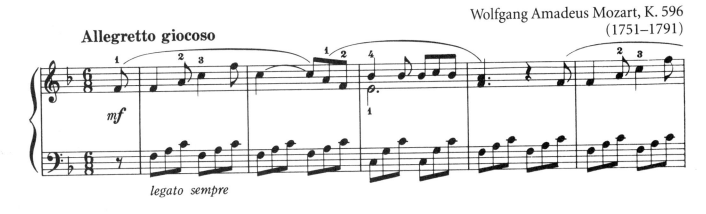

Tambourin

François Gossec
(1734–1829)

Minuet

Ludwig van Beethoven
(1770–1827)

Menuetto Da Capo

Ecossaise

Franz Schubert
(1797–1828)

Six Ecossaises

Ludwig van Beethoven
(1770–1827)

58

Für Elise

Klavierstück

Ludwig van Beethoven
(1770–1827)

Bagatelle

Ludwig van Beethoven
(1770–1827)

Rondo-Valse

Muzio Clementi
(1752–1832)

Fantasia

D minor

Wolfgang Amadeus Mozart, K. 397
(1756–1791)

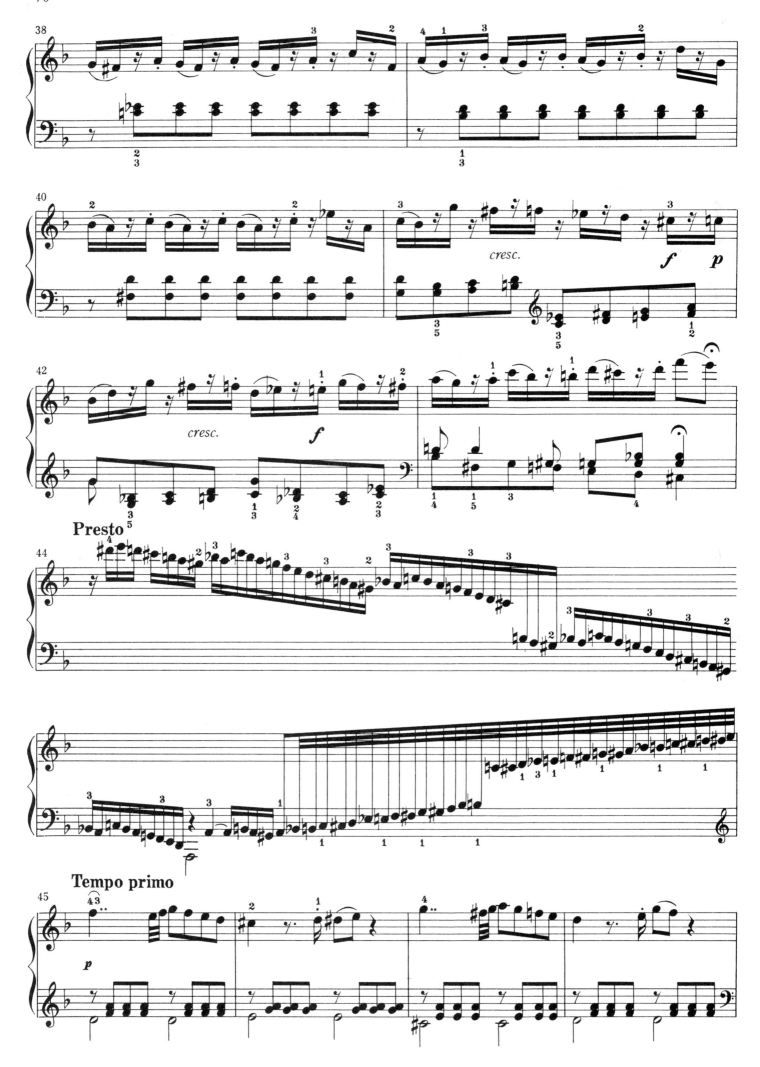

Bagatelle

Ludwig van Beethoven, Op. 119, No. 11
(1770–1827)

Alla Turca

from Sonata in A

Wolfgang Amadeus Mozart, K. 331
(1756–1791)

75

Sonatina

I

Wolfgang Amadeus Mozart
(1756–1791)

Coda

II Rondo

Sonata

quasi una Fantasia (first movement)

Ludwig van Beethoven, Op. 27, No. 2
(1770–1827)

Adagio sostenuto
Si deve suonare tutto questo pezzo delicatissimamente e senza sordini.

Scherzo

Franz Schubert, Op. posthumous
(1797–1828)

Scherzo D.C.

Impromptu

Franz Schubert, Op. 142, No. 2
(1797–1828)

Moment Musical

Franz Schubert, Op. 94, No. 3
(1797–1828)

Arabesque

Johann Friedrich Burgmüller
(1806–1874)

Allegro Scherzando

Pastorale

Johann Friedrich Burgmüller
(1806–1874)

94

Soldier's March

Robert Schumann, Op. 68, No. 2
(1810–1856)

The Wild Horseman

Robert Schumann, Op. 68, No. 8
(1810–1856)

Merry Farmer Returning from Work

Robert Schumann, Op. 68, No. 10
(1810–1856)

Rêverie

Robert Schumann, Op. 15, No. 7
(1810–1856)

Song Without Words

Felix Mendelssohn-Bartholdy, Op. 19, No. 4
(1809–1847)

99

Venetian Boat Song

Felix Mendelssohn-Bartholdy, Op. 30, No. 6
(1809–1847)

Prelude

Frédéric Chopin, Op. 28, No. 4
(1810–1849)

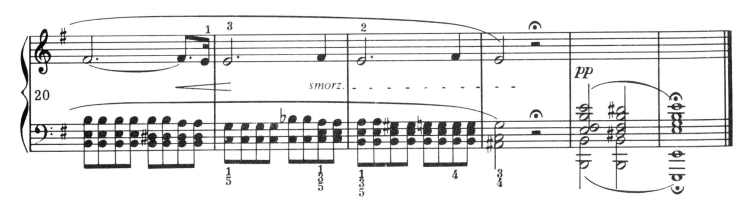

Prelude

Frédéric Chopin, Op. 28, No. 20
(1810–1849)

Prelude

Frédéric Chopin, Op. 28, No. 6
(1810–1849)

Prelude

Frédéric Chopin, Op. 28, No. 7
(1810–1849)

Mazurka

Frédéric Chopin, Op. 68, No. 2
(1810–1849)

Mazurka

Frédéric Chopin, Op. 67, No. 3
(1810–1849)

Page 109

Prelude

Frédéric Chopin, Op. 28, No. 15
(1810–1849)

Etude

Frédéric Chopin, Op. 10, No. 3
(1810–1849)

117

Valse

Frédéric Chopin, Op. 64, No. 2
(1810–1849)

Tempo giusto

122

Funeral March
from Sonata No. 2

Frédéric Chopin, Op. 35
(1810–1849)

Valse

Frédéric Chopin, Op. 69, No. 2
(1810–1849)

130

131

132

Waltz

Johannes Brahms, Op. 39, No. 15
(1833–1897)

Consolation No. 3

Franz Liszt
(1811–1886)

*These notes are additions by Emil von Sauer

Old French Song

Peter I. Tchaikovsky, Op. 39, No. 16
(1840–1893)

Moderato assai

Italian Song

Peter I. Tchaikovsky, Op. 39, No. 15
(1840–1893)

Allegretto

June

"Barcarolle" from The Seasons

Peter I. Tchaikovsky, Op. 37b, No. 6
(1840–1893)

Chanson Triste

Allegro non troppo
la melodia con molto espressione

Peter I. Tchaikovsky, Op. 40, No. 2
(1840–1893)

Norwegian Dance Melody
Nowegisch

Edvard Grieg, Op. 12, No. 6
(1843–1907)

147

Waltz

from Lyric Pieces

Edvard Grieg, Op. 12, No. 2
(1843–1907)

Allegro moderato

149

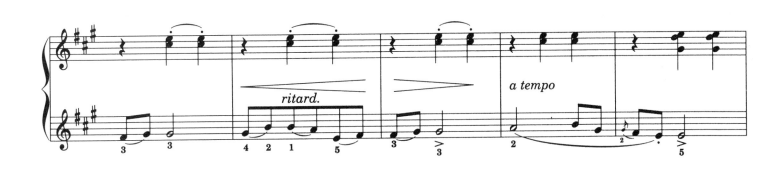

Tango

Isaac Albéniz, Op. 165
(1860–1909)

Anitra's Dance
from Peer Gynt Suite No. 1

Edvard Grieg
(1843–1907)

Tempo di Mazurka (♩ = 160)

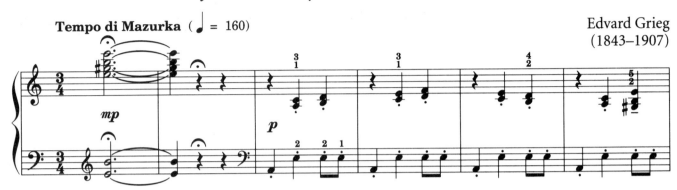

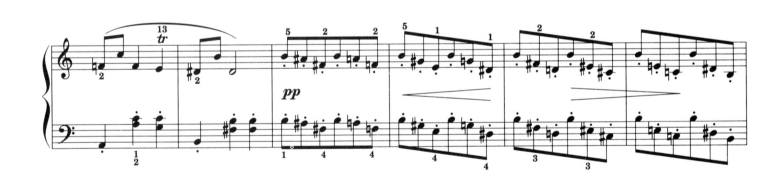

* Trills without afterbeat.

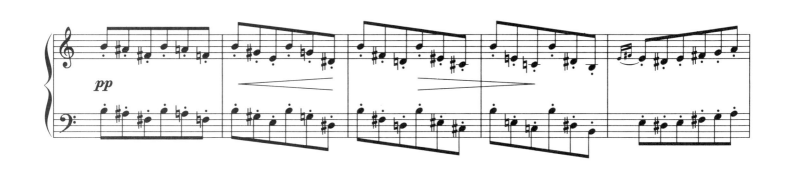
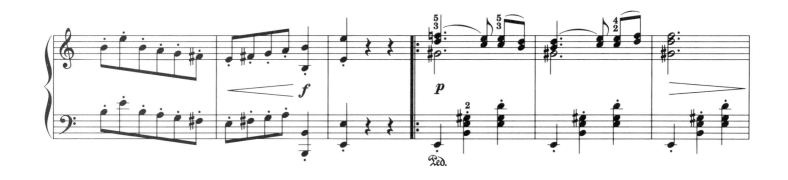

To a Wild Rose

from Woodland Sketches

Edward MacDowell
(1860–1908)

Rustle of Spring

Christian Sinding, Op. 32, No. 3
(1856–1941)

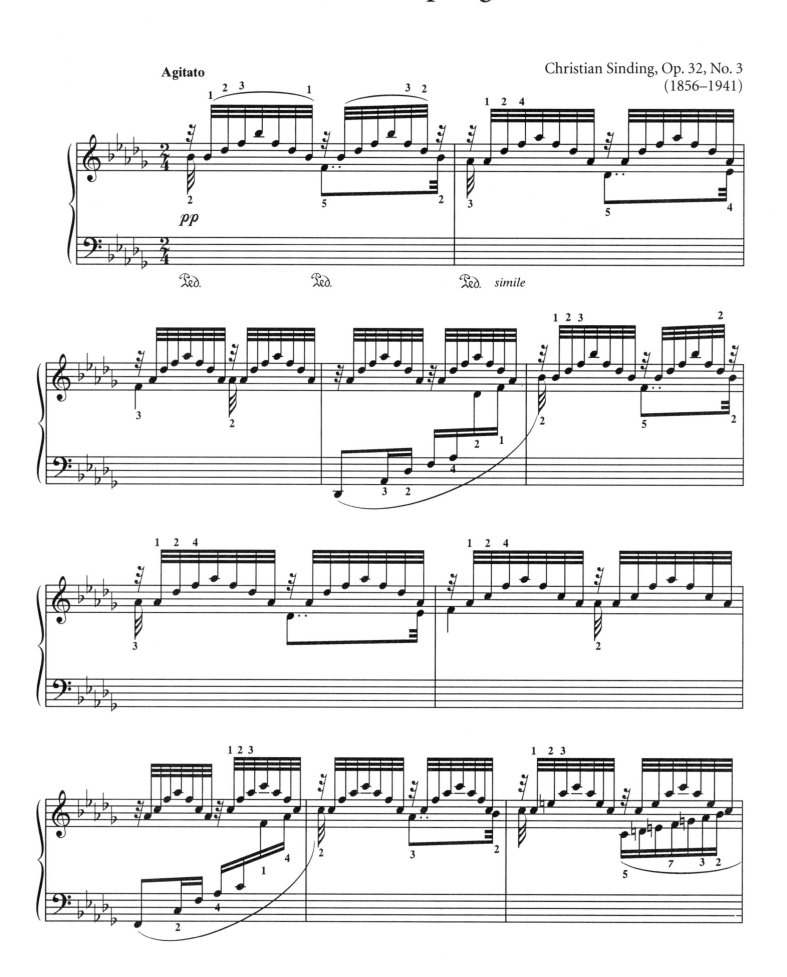

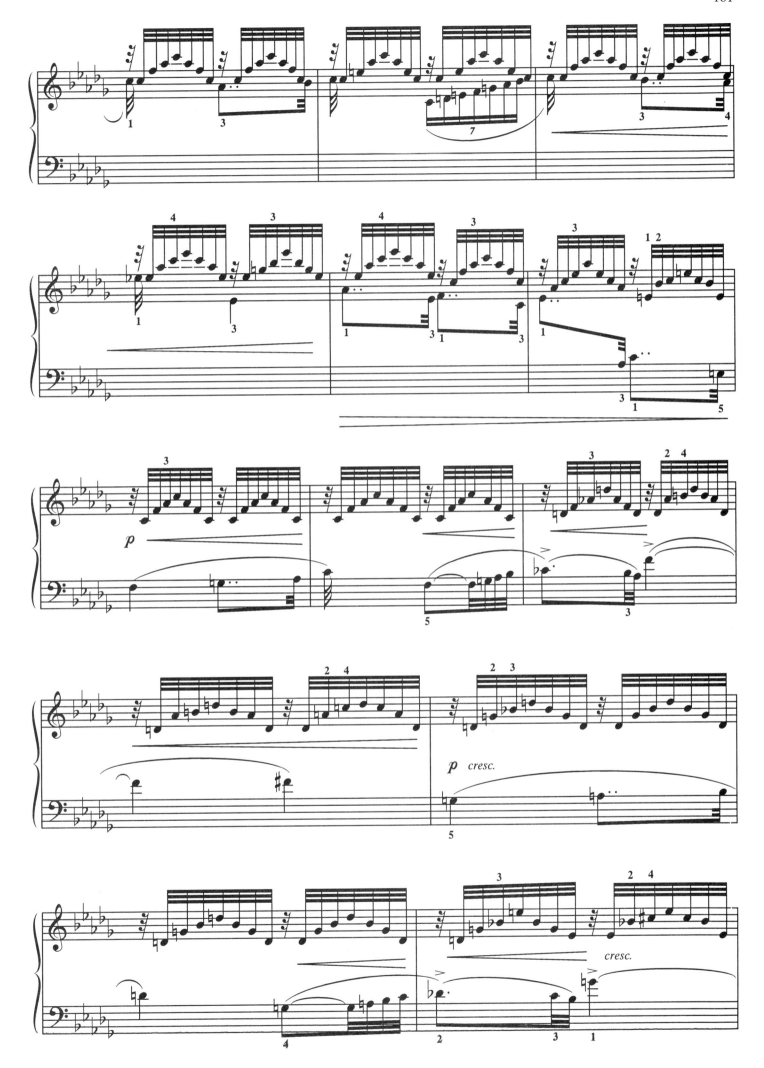

162

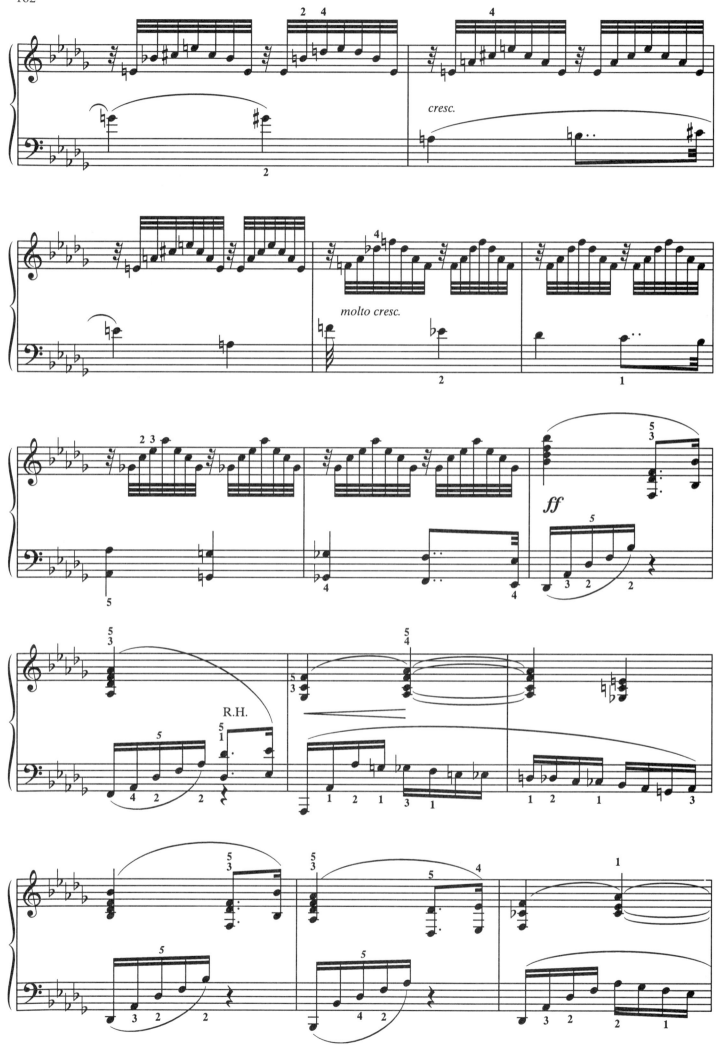

163

Spanish Dance No. 2

Moritz Moszkowksy
(1854–1925)

D. C. al Fine

Humoreske

Antonin Dvořák, Op. 101, No. 7
(1841–1904)

Original *

173

Gymnopédie

Erik Satie
(1866–1925)

The Entertainer

Scott Joplin
(1868–1917)

D.C. al Fine

Playera

Andaluza

Enrique Granados
(1867–1916)

Andantino, quasi Allegretto

The Little Negro

Le Petit Nègre

Claude Debussy
(1862–1918)

187

Lament

Béla Bartók
(1881–1945)

Clowns

Dmitri Kabalevsky
(1904–1987)

Dancing Leaves

Denes Agay
(1911–)

Lively and lightly ♩ = 60

Sonatina

Dmitri Kabalevsky, Op. 27, No. 16
(1904–1987)

Evening in the Country

Béla Bartók
(1881–1945)

The Girl with the Flaxen Hair

"La Fille Aux Cheveux De Lin" from Douze Preludes, Book I, No. 8

Claude Debussy
(1862–1918)

197

First Arabesque

Claude Debussy
(1862–1918)

Tempo rubato (un peu moins vite)

Etude
C-sharp minor

Alexander Scriabin, Op. 2, No. 1
(1872–1915)

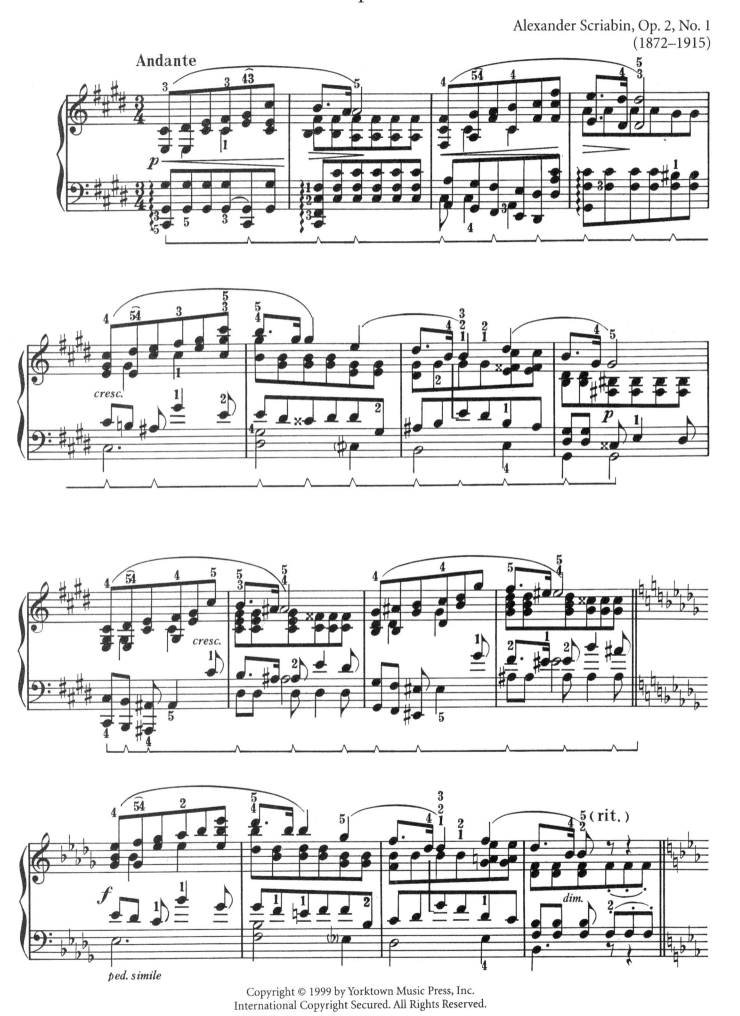

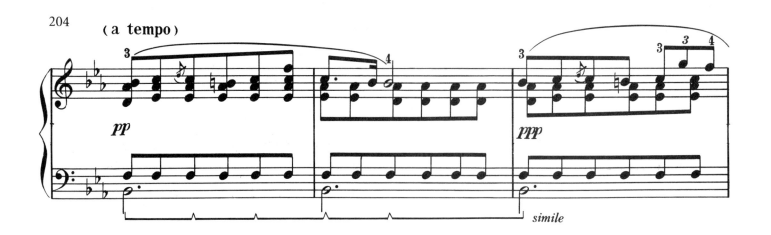

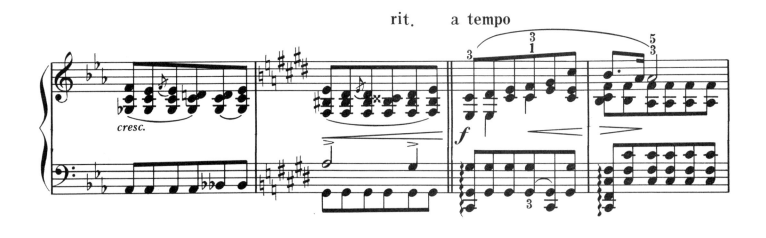

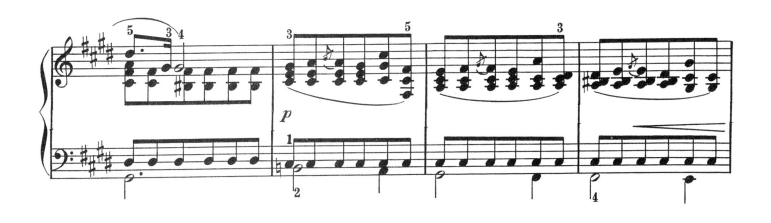

Clair de Lune
from Suite Bergamasque

Claude Debussy
(1862–1918)

pp morendo jusquà la fin

Lotus Land

Cyril Scott, Op. 47, No. 1
(1879–1970)

Bear Dance

Béla Bartók
(1881–1945)

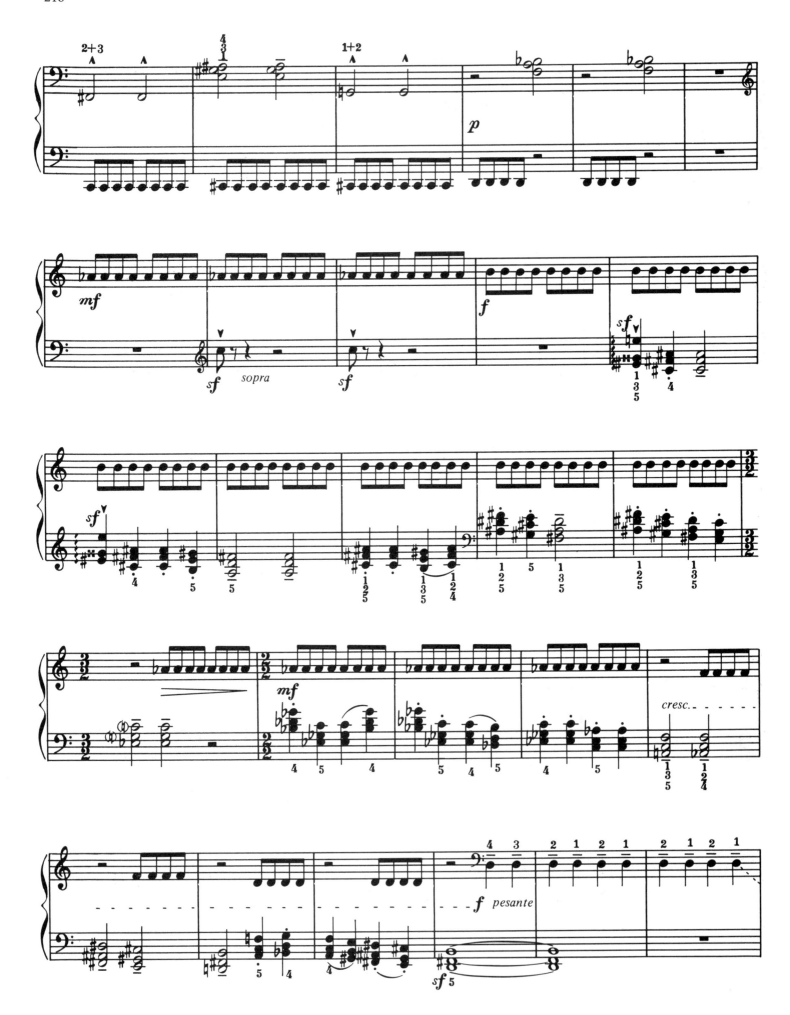

Mouvement Perpétuel No. 1

Francis Poulenc
(1899–1963)

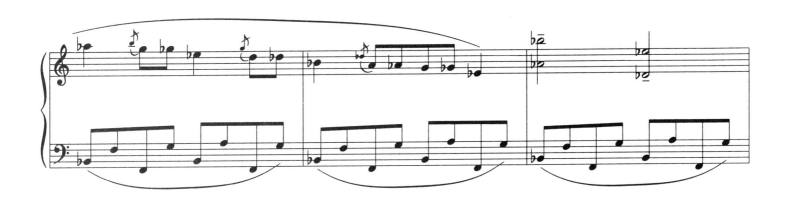

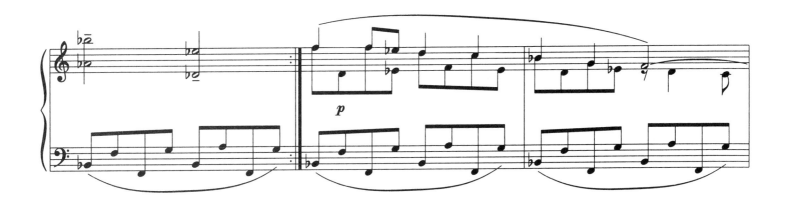

Golliwog's Cake-Walk

from Children's Corner

Claude Debussy
(1862–1918)

Un peu moins vite